MW01025576

Beyond
the
Golden Hour

How a Life of Service Saved My Life

Foxtail Books

Charlotte, North Carolina

Copyright © 2021 by Carl Stowe

All rights reserved, including the right of reproduction in
whole or in part in any form.

Printed in the United States of America

ISBN 978-0-9914443-9-7

1.Carl Stowe 2.Emergency Medical Services 3.Gaston
County, North Carolina 4.Physician Assistant 5.Vietnam
6.Medical Trauma Response 7.GEMs

Dedication

This is dedicated to my wife, Ginger, without whose love, caring, support, and encouragement there is little doubt that I would not be here today.

FORWARD

Has your job ever *literally* saved your own life?

As an EMT, a Physician Assistant, and the inaugural Chief of Crowders Mountain Volunteer Fire and Rescue, Carl Stowe dedicated his professional career to improving emergency response procedures that saved countless lives. Carl focused his energies on implementing measures which increased successful outcomes to life-threatening traumatic emergencies. From developing training programs to organizing response protocols, he single-mindedly served the needs of the good folks who live in his patch of Gaston County, North Carolina. For each distinct circumstance, for what would be that person's worst day of their life, Carl instituted trauma-response techniques that made every minute count - because every minute counts when your life is on the line.

I met Carl Stowe several years ago after my retirement from UNC-Charlotte. I was an Instructor in History and had written and published three books. When he mentioned he had a book in the works, I knew I wanted to read it because he's a natural storyteller and he had quite a story to tell.

In ***BEYOND THE GOLDEN HOUR: How a Life of Service Saved My Life,*** Carl Stowe uses charming Southern wit and humor to bring his story to life. In it, he chronicles how the Emergency Medical Service (now called GEMS) in Gaston County, North Carolina was developed. If that account alone was where the story ended, it would be a valuable contribution to Gaston County history. But Carl's story does not end there. And it's the rest of the story that will bring you chills. Carl and his family never dreamed that his every effort to improve medical knowledge and rapid emergency response would save his own life. But it did.

Read this book if you are interested in Gaston County history, but also read it for inspiration in how to face, with courage, the worst day of your life.

Marsha L Burris
Charlotte, North Carolina
March 2021

Table of Contents

Forward

Dedication

Acknowledgements

Resources

Chapter 1

The Early Years

I was born in early September 1949 in Gastonia. My hometown is a small rural spot on the map in the southern piedmont of North Carolina - about twenty miles west of Charlotte. I was the oldest of five children. As the only boy, I lived with my parents and grandparents in a house located on York Road. The building that housed the old Gaston County Department of Social Services currently stands there. Later my parents built a two-bedroom house off Crowders Creek Road in southern Gaston County on land that my father had inherited. We moved there before my sisters were born. I shared the bedroom vacated by my grandparents when they built their house across from my parents with my three sisters until my fourth sister came along relegating me to a fold-out bed in our living room. I don't need to say what kind of problems this caused when my sisters began dating, but it all worked out. My sisters are still fairly local with their own families.

As a child I dreamed of becoming a doctor and acted on that passion by bandaging cuts and scrapes and removing splinters from family members. I even practiced suturing techniques on an old foam pillow. I remember my grandfather seeking me out if he had a splinter in his finger saying that I had 'the most steady hands' of anyone he knew. So, it was not surprising that my life gravitated toward one of public service. However, there would be a number of factors that would influence how I would provide that service. It also took a life-threatening auto accident in March 2006 to show me what my service has really meant to me.

Although not very athletic, I did play on a local little league baseball team. I rotated playing outfield, first base, and third base.

Little League Team
[The author is in the middle row-far left]

I was an average student in English and Math while attending Hunter Huss High School, but I excelled in Science and Biology, as well as Music.

I played trumpet in the school band and although we did not organize a marching band while I was there, I did take my trumpet to home football games where I played the school fight song from the stands.

I played *Taps* at my grandmother's DAR (Daughter's of the American Revolution) chapter at the annual service they held on Memorial Day.

I was president of the Health Careers Club at Huss my senior year. I often wonder how many of my fellow club members actually made healthcare a career. I graduated in 1967 which was the third class to graduate from the then new school.

During my junior year I entered the school Science Fair with a model of a volcano. With the help of my Science teacher, I was able to simulate a Vesuvius-like explosion by combining potassium permanganate and glycerin. I demonstrated the process to the judges, and later one of the judges returned and called to his counterparts, 'Here it is!' He awarded me the Second-Place ribbon in the Junior Physical division.

When I was fifteen, I worked with the Gaston County Food Distribution program that provided food for low-income families. This was before Medicaid.

I saved my money, and since my father worked for Gaston County, was able to purchase a surplus, black 1956 Chevrolet for two hundred dollars. This was my first car and I bought it with money that I had earned. Being safety conscious, and before I got my driver's license at age sixteen, I purchased two sets of seatbelts and installed them myself in the front seats. I used them every time I drove my car and continue to use seatbelts to this day.

While still in high school I developed an interest in architectural drafting. I did well in these classes and thought about developing this talent into a career. After graduation, and while working as a stocker in a local supermarket, I enrolled in the Architectural Drafting program at Gaston Community College and began classes in September 1967. I graduated in August 1969. Three houses were built from my plans—one in Gastonia, another in Kings Mountain, and a third one in Myrtle Beach, South Carolina.

I was drafted into military service in September 1969, not two weeks after graduating from Gaston College. I joined the Army to become a clerk typist the day before I was scheduled to be inducted. At the time, most of the young men who were drafted in Gaston County were being sent to infantry training. I elected to join the Army in hopes that I could serve my time somewhere other than Vietnam. I ended up there anyway!

Before my deployment, while I was still in school, I had traded my 1956 Chevy for a 1963 Chevrolet Impala, which I later traded for a 1968 Chevelle. When I left for Vietnam I warned my sisters not to drive it, but that did not last long. Claudia, the older of my sisters, took my Chevelle out one night with my cousin in tow. Suddenly a water hose burst creating a large amount of steam from the engine compartment which my sister and cousin thought was smoke.

"Get out!" cried my cousin.

But my sister said, "No, if it's going to burn, I'm going with it!" I don't think they drove it anymore after that.

1968 Chevelle

Perhaps I should take a moment to tell you about my current family. Years after returning from my Vietnam tour of duty, and while working with the Cramerton Clinic in Cramerton, North Carolina, I would take after-hours calls and make rounds on our patients that we had admitted to the hospital. It was during this time, while seeing a patient in the emergency room, that I met my future wife, the beautiful Ginger Ann Bollinger, who worked there as a registered nurse.

Ginger is from Dallas.

North Carolina.

Not Texas.

We began dating, and then on January 14, 1978 we were married at the church she had attended since she was a child. This was the happiest day of my life. We put up a house across the hill from my parent's house on property that they had given us. We still live there today.

After honeymooning at Disney World in Orlando, Florida, we returned home and to work, and we began our life together.

Our first child was born in October 1979. Ginger is an only child, and I am the oldest of five children, my four siblings are girls, so I convinced Ginger that we didn't even need to consider boys names. There was no ultrasound available at the time to determine the baby's gender, but I knew it would be a girl and I was right. We named her Kelly Ann.

Ginger and I decided early on that she would stay at home with Kelly and consider returning to work after she began school.

Kelly attended South Gastonia Elementary School, then Southwest Middle School, then Hunter Huss High School, all in Gastonia. While at Hunter Huss, Kelly won both the School Pageant and Homecoming Queen in the same year. After graduating high school, Kelly attended the University of North Carolina in Chapel Hill, North Carolina. She began dating Eric Boggs, who was from Dallas, North Carolina, and also attended UNC.

I was working at Gaston Internal Medicine at the time with Eric's aunt. I saw him looking at a picture of Kelly that was on the desk I was using. We told Eric that Kelly was going to be at the local mall on a certain day. He went to meet her. They hit it off and began dating. They were married in 2002.

Kelly worked at UNC in Memorial Hall as Audience Director until she had our first grandchild in 2011. She has since become a stay-at-home Mom with two other children.

Our second child, Erin Beth, was born in August 1983. Again, Ginger and I did not even consider boys' names. I knew in my heart we would have another girl. I was right again.

I always thought that I might like to have a son, but let me tell you, I wouldn't trade either of my girls for all the boys in the world. There's nothing like having *Daddy's Girls* to teach how to fish or play baseball. To this day neither will bait a hook, but that's okay.

Erin also attended South Gastonia Elementary, Southwest Junior High, and Hunter Huss High School. Erin was also in the School Pageant at Huss and took first runner-up. She was also in the Homecoming Court after Kelly graduated.

Erin attended Appalachian State University in Boone, North Carolina where she majored in interior design. Erin graduated in 2005 and worked at Lowes in Monroe, North Carolina as an interior designer. She met Joshua Blake while in college. They dated and were married in the Chapel of my alma mater, the Medical University of South Carolina in Charleston, South Carolina.

After my accident Erin had told me, "I'm not going to get married until my daddy can walk me down the aisle."

In January of 2015 I did just that.

Holding onto her arm, I didn't even use the walking cane that I had become so dependent upon.

Erin and Joshua bought a house in Indian Land, South Carolina shortly after their son, Jackson, our fourth grandchild, was born in 2018.

My daughters are fortunate in that we were able to provide them with a debt free college education. They didn't think much about that until their college classmates became concerned about getting jobs so they could begin repaying their loans.

We are proud of our girls. Ginger and I are now empty nesters. We occupy our time watching television shows or going to see the latest movies. But our favorite thing to do is drive to Durham or Indian Land as often as possible to visit our daughters and grandchildren and babysit when we can.

One would think that with all the medical influence from Ginger and me that Kelly or Erin would end up in the medical field. Think again! Both of them said that hearing the 'war stories' from their parents was enough to make them look toward other careers.

My mother died in 2006 while I was in rehab at Courtland Terrace in Gastonia. My father died in 2010. Ginger's father died in 1994 and her mother in 2014. We do miss our parents and wish they could have lived to see their grandchildren and great-grandchildren.

Chapter 2
Military Service

As I mentioned above, I received my draft notice in September 1969. During the Vietnam War era, all eligible males in Gaston County were subject to the draft lottery. My lottery number was '10' so I didn't stand much of a chance avoiding being drafted. I decided to enlist in a delayed entry program that allowed me to defer reporting for basic training at Fort Bragg, North Carolina until January 5, 1970.

At this time, almost every young man who was drafted from Gaston County ended up in the infantry. Of course, I was worried that I would also have to go to Vietnam, however being the son of a Second World War veteran and the grandson of a World War One veteran, I never considered running to Canada to escape military service.

My basic training was at Fort Bragg, North Carolina, and my secondary training, as a clerk typist, was at Fort Jackson, South Carolina.

Afterwards I was sent to Fort Sam Houston in San Antonio, Texas, where I trained in medical records.

I was excited to go to San Antonio. I had often wished that I could see the Alamo, so after getting settled at Fort Sam, I took a bus in search of the infamous landmark. I was expecting to find it out in a desert setting surrounded by nothing but sand and tumbleweed. Was I surprised!

I stepped off the bus, and there it was, the infamous Alamo. Downtown San Antonio surrounded the entire structure. Although disappointed by its location, I made the tour anyway.

After completing the training in medical records at Fort Sam Houston, I was indeed sent to South Vietnam in August 1970. The day I left home for Vietnam, my best friend, my dog Bullet, was standing in the driveway.

The flight was nineteen hours long. We stopped in Hawaii, Wake Island, and Okinawa before the plane arrived at the replacement station in Long Binh, South Vietnam.

Aerial View of 3rd Surgical Hospital

Front of Hospital

I can remember the first several days spent in the replacement station in Long Binh. We were hit by mortar fire three nights straight. Then, once we were in Binh Thuy, we took mortar fire on my first night there. I was concerned this would be a regular occurrence.

I would be assigned to the Registrar's Office at the 3rd Surgical Hospital MA located in Binh Thuy which is in the southern part of the country along the Me Kong River near the larger city of Can Tho. As I said, my first night in Binh Thuy was marred by mortar fire but the mortar attacks in Binh Thuy proved to be few and far between after that, with only one mortar attack close to the hospital during most of my time there. Then, with three days to go before leaving Vietnam for home, we once again took mortar fire.

In 1969 the 3rd Surg was moved from its tent structures in Dong Tam into permanent structures vacated by the 29th Evacuation Hospital in Binh Thuy when it was returned to the

11

United States. A U.S. Naval base, an Air Force base, and an engineer compound surrounded us.

The 1970 film, *MASH* was shown while I was there and if I had not been in Vietnam, except for that fact that the 3rd Surg was occupying permanent buildings, I would have never believed the similarity with the movie. We had guards stationed in towers around the hospital compound at night. They were given weapons, but no ammunition! If a guard saw something suspicious, he would call the Officer of the Day who would investigate and bring ammo if needed.

I spent a year working in that hospital during which time I was cross trained as a medic. I saw and helped treat many types of injuries and illnesses.

My living space

I learned how to treat some of the less severe cases of trauma such as minor cuts, scrapes, abrasions, and sprains. I saw combat related injuries caused by gunshot wounds, shrapnel wounds from land mines, rockets, and mortars, burns from burning fuel, and white phosphorus grenades.

I also saw non-combat injuries such as those sustained from motor vehicle accidents, suicides, homicides, boating accidents, and head injuries that resulted from someone walking into the tail rotor of a helicopter.

Two soldiers drowned in a 40x60 foot above-ground swimming pool being built beside the hospital while I was there. Construction of the pool had not even been completed!

Pool under construction

Pool Completed

Even though double-feature movies were shown almost every night, the use of alcohol and drugs as an alternate form of entertainment was rampant. A group of Miss America contestants even visited once. I never did see Bob Hope.

There were times when our own soldiers were our worst enemies! For example, once when I was in the enlisted club on our compound, an engineer from a neighboring compound had been ejected from the club for disorderly conduct. Not long after his ejection an explosive device detonated beside the club. Fearing an enemy mortar or rocket attack everyone in the club hit the floor as holes were blown out of the club wall. I later learned that the explosion was not caused by enemy fire, as had first been thought, but had actually occurred when the engineer who was thrown out had gone back to his base, obtained a grenade and launched it at the club in retaliation for his exile.

Enlisted Club

The sound of helicopters bringing patients to the hospital was a common sound. A two-way radio in the ER was used to communicate with inbound medivac helicopters. Our call sign was Astro-Three. Anytime we heard that call sign we knew that a chopper carrying wounded soldiers would soon be arriving. Sometimes there was only one, at other times we had up to five. The landing pad for the helicopters was located outside the ER but was only large enough to allow two choppers to land together. Often other choppers hovered seemingly indefinitely while waiting for patients to be unloaded from the two that were on the ground.

Hospital Heliport

Hospital Heliport

From time to time my family would send care packages to me. Among other items were loaves of bread, Mom's homemade pound cake (still warm), and cans of Sun Drop. Most Carolinians know that this is one of the most popular soft drinks in the piedmont of North and South Carolina. I guarded these items as if they were gold, but I would share with my friends. My family also told me that they had not seen my dog, Bullet, since I left for Vietnam. That broke my heart. Other times I would splurge on a pizza from the Enlisted Club and go back to my room and write letters or make cassette tapes to send home.

Although I had two close calls, I received no injuries during my time in Vietnam. Once I was in a helicopter flying back to the 3rd Surg at night after having flown to Saigon earlier. Suddenly there were tracers coming toward us from the ground. One struck the side of the chopper not too far from my head. Several more struck along the tail section, but we did not go down. We were able to return to the hospital without further incident.

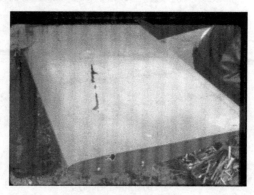

Damage to Helicopter

Helicopter Damage

Helicopter Damage

The second occurred when I was traveling by bus back to the base after a sightseeing trip to Can Tho, about twenty miles away. The bus had stopped on a bridge due to slow traffic ahead. We had been stopped for five to ten minutes when suddenly there was a burst of gunfire outside the bus. A South Vietnamese soldier assigned to guard the bridge had just shot and killed a person who was about to throw an explosive onto the bus that I, and several more soldiers, were on.

Bridge

I can remember once, after working a 24-hour shift in the ER, I was so tired that I went to my bunk and crashed. I don't know how long I slept, but when I got up, I heard several corpsmen talking about, 'how close they got last night'. I was shocked to learn of the mortar attack to which they were referring. I had yet to hear one explosion.

To this day some of the things that I saw while in Vietnam weigh heavily on my mind. The sound of a helicopter can cause me to think of my time there. I often think about a high school classmate, who I didn't even know was in Vietnam, being brought into the hospital. He was dead on arrival after having been struck by enemy fire. I never felt so helpless.

Working closely in the emergency department of the hospital with wounded soldiers and Vietnamese civilians, I developed a further interest in the medical profession, which I later learned would be my ultimate calling.

I finally received my orders to return to the States in August 1971. I believe that the emotions onboard that

18

homeward bound jet alone would have been enough to get us home. Our return flight took us over Japan and Alaska before reaching our final destination of Fort Dix, New Jersey. From there I tried to get a flight to Charlotte, but there were none available in the time I wanted so I elected to fly to Columbia, South Carolina instead. My family drove the two-hour trip and met me there.

While awaiting my flight, the call of nature became overpowering. The public toilets at the airport were all coin operated, and since I was just returning from Vietnam, I had no change. I managed to bypass the coin-operated door by crawling under it, completed my business, and crawled back out.

Some civilians showed little respect for soldiers returning from Vietnam even though we, as soldiers, were only doing our jobs. On the flight to Columbia I was sitting beside an elderly lady who seemed interested in my life until I told her that I was returning home from Vietnam at which point she didn't say another word to me. Vietnam veterans were not given the same welcome home that today's Iraqi and Afghan vets receive. We were often times spit on or physically attacked although we were just soldiers doing our part for this country.

It was early morning when we finally arrived home. It sure felt good to be there. As I stepped out of the car, there to greet me was my best friend, Bullet! He had not been seen for a year. He stayed around until I left for my new assignment never to return.

My updated orders were for me to report to New York for assignment in Germany, but I was given only five days at home after being in Vietnam for the past year. Going to Germany was not too big of a deal, but I felt like five days was not enough time at home. I contacted my Congressman and told him of the situation. He assured me that he would be able to help, but after three days he called stating that there was nothing he could do. This did not sit well with me. There had to be some way to get more time at home. As a final effort I called the Pentagon and spoke with a civilian lady in the reassignment section. I burned her ear with information of my situation. Her response was, "Well, where do you want to go?"

I knew then where the *real power* resided and I thought I would faint. After a few minutes we had decided that I would be assigned to Kenner Army Hospital in Fort Lee, Virginia. I received thirty days leave to boot.

The new assignment placed me only a few hours' drive down I-85 to get home. I bought a new 1972 Chevelle, Mediterranean Blue, with black racing stripes, a black vinyl top, and black interior. Beautiful car! I drove home every weekend.

1972 Chevelle

On December 31, 1971, I was part of a team to accompany a group of disabled Vietnam veterans to Pasadena, California, to see the Tournament of Roses Parade and later the Rose Bowl football game between Michigan and Stanford. This was quite exciting. At the parade, we were seated just in front of the CBS review booth which was manned by none other than Bob Barker. We flew back to Virginia after the events.

Later in January 1972, I was released from active duty to serve the remainder of my military obligation in an Army Reserve hospital unit in Charlotte, North Carolina. There I would go to the Army Reserve base once a month until discharged. I was also required, as part of the reserve unit, to spend a two-week period on active duty which I did at Fort Benning, Georgia.

My family drove down to meet me at Fort Benning at the end of my first week. After being granted weekend leave, we drove down to the Florida Gulf coast, stayed two nights, and returned to Fort Benning before returning to Charlotte with my unit.

I received an Honorable Discharge from active duty in September 1972.

Chapter 3

Fire Service

Before and after my military service, and in addition to work and school, my personal interest in public service guided me to join the South Gastonia Volunteer Fire Department.

In the early 1960s my father was part of the formation of two volunteer fire departments in Gaston County. The first would be called Chapel Grove VFD and, a few years later, the second was South Gastonia VFD. I went with my father to pick up Chapel Grove's first fire truck. It was an older truck purchased from a local VFD that was going out of business due to annexation of the area by the City of Gastonia. I wasn't old enough to drive, but I could operate the pump on that truck as good as any fireman.

A previous attempt had been made to organize a South Gastonia VFD in the 1950s. I don't have much information on this department other than I remember their station was a shed located at the north end of what was the Myers mill on US 321 South. I remember them having one fire truck. I also do not know when it dissolved.

South Gastonia VFD would provide fire protection for the area that included our house. During the construction of the fire station I helped with pulling wiring, laying tile, and painting.

Although I was too young to be involved in fire suppression my close association daily operations sparked an interest and love for the fire services that lives today.

Our house was only a short distance from the fire station, and each night I would lie awake in bed and listen when the fire siren sounded and I would think, *One day I will be a fire fighter, too.*

When my dad would let me, I would respond with him to some calls on non-school nights. I stood beside the fire truck wearing a fire helmet and a turnout coat —way too big for me— watching as the firemen fought the fires. I would also help wash trucks and work around the fire station until I was old enough to join the South Gastonia department at age seventeen.

South Gastonia VFD Members

[The author is in the back row - 2nd from left]

One day, my dad and the department chief went to pick up our new fire truck. On that same day, I was riding the school bus home. I looked behind us and saw my dad and the department chief in that shiny new fire truck. I wasted no time getting off that bus at the next stop and ran back to get on the new truck. That truck cost seventeen thousand dollars, new. In 1998, the last truck that I was involved in purchasing for Crowders Mountain Fire and Rescue was over three hundred thousand dollars!

The department depended on donations from the community to stay in business. Each May, firefighters would go door to door in the community asking for donations of at least ten dollars. To identify those who contributed, we would drive a white wooden stake with a red flag stapled to it in the ground near their driveway.

I came up through the ranks. In 1995, as Assistant Chief, I was appointed to a committee formed by Gaston County to merge three volunteer fire departments that included members from each department. South Gastonia, Chapel Grove, and Chestnut Ridge VFD were to merge into one department.

County officials thought that this merger would save taxpayers money in the long run. The name of this new department would be Crowders Mountain Volunteer Fire and Rescue.

A local rescue squad, Bessemer City Rescue, in Bessemer City, North Carolina, was operating out of a building so small that it had no place for equipment. These vehicles had to be parked outside. We were going to offer the rescue squad a bay in our new building, but their Board of Directors instead asked to join the merger. We had never thought that the squad would want to join us in the merger but were glad to include them.

Bessemer City Rescue had been given a vacated bank building in Bessemer City which would later be renovated to allow equipment for the newly formed department to be housed safely in bays.

It was difficult for the different entities to agree on all the aspects of the merger. There were many ups and downs. Chestnut Ridge eventually withdrew from the merger process. The renovations on the Bessemer City station was already well under way, so the committee decided to continue the renovations even though the station would be at the northern end of the district without Chestnut Ridge.

The merger became official on July 1, 2000 borrowing the name of Crowders Mountain, the 1,624-foot tall mountain icon that lies within our fire district. Crowders Mountain is now a North Carolina State Park.

North Station

Central Station

South Station

I was elected the inaugural Chief by the Board of Directors for this new department and served in that position until January 2002. I remained on the active role as a firefighter until my accident in 2006. After my term as Chief, I was elected to the Board of Directors where I was given the job of Chairman of our Building Committee.

New Station

Working with other members of our department and a local architect, we designed and built a new station. This station

28

would allow for the closure and sale of the old Central and South stations leaving us with a new station: Station 1 and a renovated one: Station 2. While I was on the active role, I performed tasks such as entering report data into a data base for several years. But as a result of the life-threatening injuries, I received in an automobile accident, it was impossible for me to respond to calls. I retired after 43 years with the volunteer fire service.

Chapter 4
Emergency Service

Before I began my work with Gaston County Emergency Medical Services [GEMS] but after my discharge from active military service, I needed to find a job. I was unaware of the existence of Physician Assistants programs at the time, so using my home design experience, I found a job with a local interior design firm. Sometime later in 1972 I took a position as an ambulance attendant for Gaston County thereby continuing my desire to work in medicine.

My initial medical training was in Advanced First Aid, the forerunner of today's Emergency Medical Technician (EMT). Our ambulances at the time were Ford station wagons outfitted with a stretcher. These vehicles had previously been used in dual service with the Gaston Rural Police during a time when the police provided ambulance service for Gaston County.

Although I had been trained in some emergency medical procedures while in the Army, I had to become certified in Advanced First Aid, then eventually as an EMT. After certification I worked at several ambulance stations that were located in different parts of the county.

Sat., April 29, 1972

Old County Ambulance

In mid-1972 I was working directly with patients providing care for a variety of illnesses and injuries. Looking to improve my patient care skills, I eventually became one of the first state-certified Emergency Medical Technicians for Gaston County. I was directly involved in treating a variety of medical conditions and traumatic injuries prior to delivering the patient to a hospital. It was difficult to say the least. Imagine doing CPR on a stretcher in the back of a station wagon once operated by the police!

The history of emergency medical services in Gaston County is interesting in that it's full of twists and turns. Until the 1960s local funeral homes and volunteer rescue squads provided ambulance service for Gaston County. Rescue squads also provided rescue when needed such as extrication from an accident. These two groups would respond when called either directly by a patient or dispatched by an emergency dispatcher. Sometimes an ambulance from both a local funeral home and one from a local rescue squad would arrive on the scene of an accident at the same time. This could result in conflict over who was going to transport the patient.

In order to improve the quality of care, and because of the ineffectiveness of the current system, Gaston County Commissioners delegated emergency medical care to the Gaston County Rural Police. This move would assure the availability of ambulance transportation 24-hours daily.

Two police officers, calling themselves *Medicops,* and trained in Advanced First Aid would respond to medical calls in addition to their patrol duties. The funeral homes and rescue squads continued to handle non-emergency medical calls. Far from ideal, this system was wrought with problems. Therefore, in an attempt to improve ambulance service, the County Commissioners moved oversight of all ambulance service from the police department to the newly formed office of Gaston County Emergency Management in the early 1970s.

The new configuration of services allowed the police to concentrate solely on law enforcement. The funeral homes eventually discontinued providing ambulance service, but there would always be a need for the volunteers.

In addition to my volunteer work as an EMT, I had other opportunities to apply my medical skills. My father had several goats that he allowed to roam over his property. One day I noticed that one of the goats had broken its left front leg below the knee. I called a friend of mine, Koppie Williams, who also worked as an EMT for Gaston County. Together we formulated a plan for treatment. We went to the X-ray department at Gaston Memorial Hospital where we knew one of the X-ray technicians. We obtained some casting material and returned to my father's house. We took the goat to the barn, rigged up a belly-sling that allowed us to raise the goat's front legs off the ground and applied a cast to the goat's broken leg. I let the goat out of the sling the next day and to my surprise she seemed to be able to walk without too much difficulty. The goat actually used the heavy cast to her advantage by using it to pull down low tree limbs so that she could eat the leaves. It was really quite humorous. After about six weeks I removed the cast and except for a slight external rotation of its hoof was able to walk very well.

I learned a lot about patient care, both human and animal, in my time with the ambulance service and hoped that the experience would help me in my pursuit of a career in medicine.

In mid-1973 Gaston County turned the task of providing ambulance services over to the county's eight volunteer rescue squads when somehow the volunteers convinced the Commissioners that they could do the job at no cost to taxpayers. The Commissioners at that time seemed more interested in saving money and therefore dissolved the county supported ambulance service. Overnight the EMTs staffing the county ambulances were without a job. But by this time, I had moved to the Communications Division, so I didn't lose mine.

This was the pre-911 era in Gaston County. I worked in a ten by twelve-foot room that had space for two radio operators. Communications for all of Gaston County, excluding the City of Gastonia Police, were handled from that room. This included all fire, EMS, Gaston County Rural Police, police calls for three of the nine small towns in Gaston County, and the Gaston County local government channel. We had no computers, therefore all data was hand-written on 3 x 9-inch data cards.

Gastonia City Police handled calls by radio for police and fire inside the city limits, however, calls for emergency medical services were passed on to the county. When a county police unit needed information about an automobile or an individual driver's license, we had to call the Gastonia Police dispatcher for this information. Since they were fortunate enough to have a PIN (Police Information Network) computer they would furnish us with the requested information. Eventually Gaston County upgraded communications equipment and I was sent to Raleigh and trained to become the first PIN operator for Gaston County. I then trained our other dispatchers to use the PIN system.

The North Carolina Highway Patrol investigated all motor vehicle accidents (MVA) in the unincorporated areas of Gaston County. Their dispatch center monitored our police radio frequency and we monitored theirs. When we received a call for an MVA we called the Highway Patrol over our police radio frequency then listened for their response on their radio receiver.

Frequently I found myself alone during an entire 8-hour shift. I sat in that small room surrounded by twenty-four radio receivers, four transmitters, and two incoming phone lines answering calls about fires, shootings, burglaries, motor vehicle accidents, and requests for medical help among other things. From this room I would dispatch the appropriate police, fire, or ambulance unit to handle the call for help. I might find myself coordinating vehicle chases for police, listening as firefighters battled structure and brush fires and, since there was no radio communication with the local hospital, notifying them when an ambulance was en route to their location with a critical patient.

A shift alone in the communications room could be quite harrowing depending on the incoming call type and volume. This was exciting at times, but it still did not satisfy my itch for patient care involvement.

I left the communications service in September 1974 to join the Gaston County Rural Police department as a police officer.

Chapter 5

Police Years

While working as a dispatcher I became interested in law enforcement. I applied for a position with the Gaston County Police Department and was accepted.

After graduating from the Police Rookie School at Gaston College in 1974, and still single, I began my career as a patrol officer. I was involved in countless investigations including many violent crimes.

I don't remember writing traffic citations often. I always felt that I could not write a citation for something that I might, on occasion, be guilty of myself. I did stop a lot of traffic violators, but as long as the driver understood the reason for being stopped, I usually let them off with a warning unless I thought they were intoxicated. If I thought the person I had stopped was under the influence I took the case to court. With one exception.

I was on patrol with another officer with whom I had attended Rookie School. A car passed us going the opposite direction. There was a male driving with a female passenger. I noticed that the car was swerving badly into oncoming traffic and turned around to catch up to and stop the car. I turned on my blue lights and siren. He was not driving fast, but it seemed that the driver was paying us no attention. He finally pulled into a convenience store parking lot. My partner was quickly out of the patrol car and brought the driver to the back of his car and began a field sobriety test. I stuck my head inside the car but smelled no alcohol. I asked his passenger if the driver had been drinking.

"No, Sir!," she said. "He has the sugar!"

Because of my medical training, I realized that the driver was diabetic and that his blood sugar was low. He recognized this and was stopping at the convenience store to buy something to raise his sugar level.

While my partner kept the driver at the car I went into the convenience store and bought him some orange juice and a candy bar. After consuming the juice and candy the driver felt much better. He refused any medical care. I called his wife to come to the scene to pick him up. She said that this was a frequent problem and was appreciative that we were able to help. His passenger, who was a co-worker, drove off in her car.

One of the last DWI arrests that I made was on a man who had eleven previous DWI arrests and twelve previous arrests for driving without a license. He had never served one day in jail for his crimes. Until now.

At trial, the prosecution was able to convince the judge that the defendant showed no intent to stop drinking then driving. He was given two years active jail time. Not enough, but better than nothing and more than he had received in the past.

My time as a police officer was not without incident. Several times during my time in law enforcement I found myself in the news. I can remember arresting a man on a warrant for passing a worthless check. He was sitting on the front porch of his house when I arrived at his home to serve the warrant. He had been drinking heavily but gave me no trouble. I served the warrant and took him to jail. The man was about five and a half feet tall and weighed 150 pounds max. The jailer was much, much bigger — over six feet tall and more than 200 pounds. The jailer asked the man his name and received it. However, when asked his age the man said in a slurred voice, "I ain't gon'a tell ya."

The next thing I saw was the jailer physically assaulting my prisoner as he was being taken to a jail cell. After discussing the situation with my supervisors, I returned to the jail to check on the prisoner. He now had a gaping laceration over his left eye which he said happened when the same jailer hit him with the jail cell keys.

I took the prisoner to the hospital where eleven stitches were required to close the wound. Feeling that police officers were not above the law, and after consulting my supervisor, I charged the jailer with assault. Needless to say, I was not popular with the Sheriff's Department.

This incident made the local paper for several days. The jailer was convicted of the assault in court, but he did not lose his job. He was actually promoted to sergeant.

I enjoyed being a police officer, and I can truthfully say that I never lost a court case. If I charged someone with a crime it stuck. However, working eight hour swing shifts and extremely long work weeks were difficult. The shifts were comprised of two consecutive weeks that included seven days on and two days off, followed by a week of seven days on and three days off. That was not much fun. Additionally, there was none of the patient contact that I longed for. I knew that I would not make law enforcement my career.

In early 1974, while in Police Rookie School, I attended a family function. I spoke with a relative, who happened to be a physician. He informed me about the Physician Assistant program at the Medical University of South Carolina in Charleston.

A Physician Assistant (PA) is a midlevel practitioner who is trained by doctors to provide some of the routine care for patients leaving the physician time to spend on more complicated patients.

The primary focus of a PA at that time was to improve access to medical care in underserved areas. My relative thought that with my military training and experience, I would be a good candidate for admission to this program. This sounded interesting to me. I was one of several hundred individuals who applied for admission to one of the thirty-six positions available for the upcoming class.

I knew that if I was accepted into the PA program, I would not make law enforcement a career, but would transfer my police certification to the Gaston County Police Reserve and could work twenty hours monthly as a volunteer police officer. I did just that until 1989 when I finally hung up my pistol belt.

Chapter 6

Physician Assistant School

After several in-person interviews over two days at MUSC, I left Charleston feeling that I had little chance of being accepted. Several months went by with no news from Charleston. Then one afternoon a letter arrived from the school. My pulse was racing as I opened the letter. It read:

Dear Mr. Stowe, This is to inform you that you have been accepted....

That's as far as I read! This was the most exciting moment of my life. In September of 1975 I would begin to fulfill the life-long dream of entering the medical world as a trained professional.

I began preparing myself for the move to Charleston. There were no dormitory rooms available for PA students, so I looked for an apartment. After an exhaustive search I settled on renting one side of a duplex at 1711 Savannah Highway, about five miles from the school. The apartment was being vacated by a graduating PA student.

My GI Bill benefits paid for tuition and books, but my rent was coming entirely out of my pocket. Luckily, it seemed that the money I had saved along with some from my parents would be enough to cover my living expenses.

I settled into my new home, and I was now ready to start classes. Little did I know what lay ahead of me.

The didactic portion of the program lasted ten months. The remaining portion of the program would be working with a physician preceptor somewhere. The preceptor, a licensed physician, would oversee my work in a clinical setting. But where I would go was yet to be determined.

During the didactic phase of the course my classmates and I were in a classroom from 8am until 5pm and were expected to observe and participate in clinical rotations after some classes and weekends.

The curriculum workload proved to be difficult. As I said, I had classes Monday thru Friday, 8 to 5, clinical rotations for several hours afterwards, then outside class work to do before classes started back the next morning. Many weekends were also occupied with clinical rotations. The load was heavy enough that several students dropped out by the end of the first two weeks.

I made friends with several fellow students, and we would gather at my apartment to hold study sessions that sometimes lasted until after midnight. Somehow, we found a way to be back in class bright and early the next morning.

Although the class work was hard and, the hours we had to devote to the course were long, we still found time for some recreation. Several of us went crabbing in the inlet behind our classrooms or fishing on Sullivan's Island or the Isle of Palms. We would then take our catch back to my apartment for a meal of seafood. We also made several trips to Myrtle Beach to test the fishing there.

My last six months of school were spent in Cramerton, North Carolina in family practice with Dr. William F. Eckbert who acted as my preceptor.

After graduating from PA school in November 1976 I accepted a position as a PA medical provider with Dr. Eckbert at the Cramerton Clinic. This was a Family Practice clinic. My duties included examining, diagnosing, and providing treatment for our patients. I was the second PA to be employed in Gaston County behind Gary Reynolds who worked for a while with a physician in Bessemer City. During the time I worked at the clinic I became the first PA to be granted practice privileges at Gaston Memorial Hospital.

In early 1983 Dr. Eckbert talked of retiring so I began looking for another job. Ginger and I had been married for about five years at this point. We already had our first daughter, Kelly, and it was about this time that Ginger became pregnant with our second child.

I was still interested in emergency response care and there were few instructors available to teach the classes. I contacted the Continuing Education Department at Gaston College and inquired about instructor positions. While continuing to work as a PA in Cramerton, I accepted a part-time staff position with the college and began instructing Emergency Medical

Technician courses. I continued working with Dr. Eckbert until the end of May 1983.

Chapter 7

Cramerton Clinic Years

The Cramerton Clinic had been a two-physician practice owned by Dr. William F. Eckbert and Dr. Rufus Davis. Dr. Davis left for employment at the VA hospital in Salisbury, North Carolina several months prior to my employment. This action caused an increase in the need for an additional provider because of the workload increase for Dr. Eckbert.

I was to begin my employment, as the second Physician Assistant in Gaston County, at the Cramerton Clinic after completing the Physician Assistant course at the Medical University of South Carolina in Charleston in 1976. However, I missed my entire first week after contracting influenza while packing to come home. When I was finally able to work, I began seeing only a few patients each day. I had to explain to every patient what a PA is and my qualifications. Amazingly, only a few patients refused to see me. With a few years' experience, patients became comfortable with me. Some even called me 'doctor'. There were some patients who had rather see me than Dr. Eckbert. I reminded them that I was not a doctor, but some continued to use that word. I said: "Okay, if you insist, as long as you know the difference."

I was needed to help with hospital rounds on our patients who were admitted to Gaston Memorial Hospital. There were no PAs on staff at GMH, so I had to apply for staff privileges, but first I had to get approval from the Director of Nursing. As a PA, I had to work from a list of standing orders that Dr. Eckbert and I had developed. I prepared a list of standing orders to be used on patients admitted to the hospital that I would follow. These were problem specific, meaning that I would order tests and treatment based on the patient's symptoms, then make changes based on the results of the tests or changes in the patient's condition.

I worked on these orders for a few weeks and they were approved by Dr. Eckbert. I took them to a meeting with the Director of Nursing and presented them to her.

"These are not specific enough," she said. I asked what she wanted. She said that she wanted to see orders for every condition that might be admitted to the hospital.

Suspecting that something like that might happen, I took out a 1976 edition of *Conn's Current Therapy* from my brief case and presented them as my orders.

"These are too specific," she said.

I asked, "What do you want?"

She eventually accepted the previous orders which meant that I was approved for staff privileges and would help make rounds in the evenings after office hours.

During my time at the Cramerton Clinic, I was fortunate enough to find several life-threatening conditions on some of our patients before they became symptomatic. I picked up at least fourteen asymptomatic abdominal aneurysms on patients who came in for complete physical exams. One lady had a subclavian steal. This is a narrowing of the artery which runs beneath the clavicle and decreases blood flow to the right or left arm causing a low blood pressure reading in the affected arm and can result in amputation of the limb if it goes uncorrected. The aneurysms were found by feeling the abdomen and the vascular abnormality was found because of a lower blood pressure in the affected arm and hearing a bruit, a whooshing sound made in the neck as blood passes through a narrowed area in an artery. All of these patients had surgery to correct their conditions, and when I left employment at the clinic all were doing well.

Dr. Eckbert continued talking about retiring. He was already in his mid-sixties. I was sad to hear that because I really liked working there. Nonetheless, I continued to think about other employment. By this time Gaston Memorial Hospital had a Physician Assistant working with the physician group contracted to provide service in the emergency room. I spoke with him, and as luck would have it, they were looking for two PAs to help with the workload. At the time GMH had the second busiest ER in the state.

After being hired by the ER group, I started there in June 1983.

Chapter 8
Time for Change

As I look back at the forty-three years of being active in the fire service, I am reminded of the first fire related fatality I saw. That is something not easily forgotten. At 3:15pm on December 27, 1969, my department was dispatched to a house fire about one mile south of our station. I knew that the fire was bad because smoke was visible in the sky as I reached the intersection of Crowders Creek Road and U.S. 321 South, a mile and a half north of the fire. Our pumper had already responded as I reached the fire station, so I stopped to pick up our tanker truck. This is a truck that carries at least one thousand gallons of water to pump to the pumper truck. The tanker was our only supply of water since there were no fire hydrants in the area.

Once on the scene, I saw that the fire was intense. I began hooking the tanker truck to the pumper and was too busy to notice what occurred inside the house. Once the fire was extinguished, I learned that there were four children still inside. All of them were deceased and under the age of ten.

It was quite cold that day. We learned from a child who escaped the fire that their mother was away at a neighbor's house, and one of the older children tried to heat up their coal burning furnace by pouring gasoline onto it. The blast from the igniting gasoline forced the other children into a back room and blocked their escape. All four were found huddled together in the back bedroom. There was a window in the room that was no more than five feet above the ground, but it appeared that no attempt had been made to escape through this window.

That all four children had died was a tragedy, but what made it even worse, their mother was pregnant and miscarried as a result of the tragedy. I had known all of them, including their parents. Since that time, I have been on the scene of three other multiple fatality fires, all involved children, but I can remember just about every detail of that first one.

Another unforgettable incident occurred in early August 1979. This was several years after I had completed my education as a Physician Assistant, and while working in family practice. My fire department was dispatched around 7 am to a house fire. I responded with our tanker and was the third truck to arrive on the scene. Upon my arrival I was told that there were people inside the house which was heavily involved in fire. I called our communications center by radio advising them of the situation and requested an emergency ambulance. At the time, all the emergency ambulance calls in Gaston County were answered by one of the eight volunteer rescue squads. Another firefighter relieved me on the tanker and I went to see if I could render aide to any of the victims. As I approached the house the first victim was brought out of a bedroom window, an infant who was not breathing and had no pulse. I immediately started CPR. Then a second child was brought out. Again, there was no pulse or breathing. Another firefighter began CPR. An adult was next to be brought out, but she was severely burned. She had no pulse and could not be saved. Finally, a third child was brought out with no pulse. Another available firefighter started CPR. When the flames were extinguished, we had six firefighters performing CPR on three children.

The first ambulance didn't arrive on the scene for forty-five minutes. That unit came from Dallas Rescue, some twelve to fifteen miles from the scene. This incident is important because it was the catalyst for changing the flaws in the current EMS system. An ambulance from the closest squad, about five miles away, could not respond immediately because there was no one available to get an ambulance, but did once members became available. The first arriving ambulance transported the first child and me to the hospital. The trip took another eight to ten minutes. Other units followed. By the time we arrived at the ER nearly one hour had passed since CPR had begun. With no obvious response to the resuscitation efforts from any of the children, doctors halted further attempts. I had long feared that something of this magnitude would happen. I felt that EMS priorities needed to be improved. Instead of sending volunteers as primary responders to emergency calls the county needed a service available twenty-four hour daily dedicated to emergencies allowing the volunteers to handle the non-emergency calls and assist on emergency calls.

Although ambulance service in Gaston County could not be provided without the aid of the volunteers, emergency service should be provided by professionally trained employees with back up service from volunteers to assure 24/7 availability of an ambulance. I cited that volunteers are just that, and like myself, all volunteers, whether they were firefighters or rescue squad personnel, had to work and meet other obligations making it impossible to guarantee 24/7 availability.

I was upset with the system as it was. At one time Gaston County operated a 24-hour emergency ambulance service. I had been part of that system, but it was halted years earlier when the rescue squads convinced the County Commissioners that the squads could do the same job at no cost to the taxpayers. Had that service still been in place an ambulance could have responded from a satellite station as close as one mile away. Unfortunately, even if an ambulance had been sitting at the scene at the time the first child was handed out of the window, the end result would probably have been the same. But that did not excuse a forty-five-minute response time for an emergency ambulance.

The news media got wind of the incident. I was contacted by a local television station for an interview. I blamed the current EMS system for its failure to provide quicker response. Some members of the rescue squads took my comments as a direct attempt to put them out of business. Nothing could have been further from the truth. I was also a volunteer. I wanted the county to re-establish the full-time emergency ambulance service it once supported so that emergency ambulance service would again be more readily available. This created quite an uproar. Several of the ER nurses who either helped with EMT classes or supported my stand on improving EMS were physically assaulted or had their property vandalized. One ER physician found a threatening letter in the mailbox outside his home. I received threatening phone calls. The police took these threats seriously. At one time there was an officer in my living room trying to trace the calls. No suspects were ever identified for any of the incidents. During this time my wife, Ginger, was pregnant with our first child and worked as a nurse in the ER at Gaston Memorial. I need not point out how upsetting these incidents were to her!

Not until 1982 did the County Commissioners respond to the concerns. They finally re-established the office of Emergency Management and assigned it the responsibility of overseeing emergency communications, the Fire Marshall's Office, and providing ambulance service, to be known as Gaston County Medical Transport (GCMT), for all non-emergency transports. This was staffed by full-time EMTs, eight-to-five, Monday through Friday, while still leaving the bulk of the emergency calls to the volunteer rescue squads. The full-time crew would only respond to an emergency call if there were no rescue squad ambulances available. This was better than nothing, but it seemed that the county's emphasis on emergency calls was misplaced. Politics! This is no place for politics!

During the years that followed the county-operated service hired a Training Officer. This person became interested in training personnel to the EMT-Intermediate level. An EMT-I can perform a number of more advanced medical procedures including insertion of an esophageal obturator airway (EOA), application of mobile anti-shock trousers (MAST), administering epinephrine by injection to victims of anaphylactic (allergic) shock, and starting IV fluids if so ordered by an ER physician. Finally, a breakthrough towards improvement. Classes were started for the GCMT employees. Before the first EMT-I class was completed the Training Officer left for other employment. I was contacted by the County EMS Director and asked if I would assume the training duties for GCMT. I accepted the position on a part-time basis with the understanding that another full-time person be hired and I began the task of training GCMT personnel to a higher level of certification. By this time, I was working as a Physician Assistant in the ER at Gaston Memorial Hospital (GMH) and I performed my EMS training duties on my off days.

The first EMT-I class was conducted for seven employees who staffed three ambulances with one supervisor.

The volunteer rescue squads were having trouble responding to the volume of calls they were being asked to answer.

The volunteer providers were doing a great job, but members could not each be available all of the time. They also had families, work, and a life outside the rescue squads that needed to come before running calls. It finally became clear to Commissioners that a true full-time ambulance provider was needed. With help from the North Carolina Office of Emergency Medical Services (NCOEMS) the full-time service was gradually expanded and assumed more of the responsibility for emergency calls.

Equipment was purchased and installed in the ER allowing for EKG strips to be sent via radio telemetry to the ER where an ER physician could view the rhythm. An EMT-I cannot defibrillate a lethal cardiac rhythm in the field, but they are able to start an IV line thus allowing for medication to be given immediately upon arrival at the ER.

Gaston County now saw the benefit of advanced pre-hospital training and the need to provide more. Interest was also rising for personnel to be trained to the EMT-Paramedic (EMT-P) level allowing patients to receive some of the same care given to patients in emergency rooms but started before they actually reach the ER. The potential impact on the survival rate was astronomical.

With the help of the physicians in the ER at Gaston Memorial and physicians from other specialties I initiated the first EMT-P program for Gaston County through Gaston

College. All of the classes, whether taught by a physician or me, were videotaped for later use as continuing education. The first EMT-Paramedic in Gaston County began in July 1987, eight years after concerns were raised about the level and availability of pre-hospital emergency care.

The Emergency Management director contacted me and said that he felt a name change for the service was in order. GCMT no longer seemed appropriate. One night my wife and I were in our living room discussing the idea when she said, "Why don't you call it Gaston County Emergency Medical Services, GEMS."

"That's a wonderful name," I said, and presented the idea to the Director. He said we would be the *Gems of the County*. Thus, a new service was born.

Another full-time Training Officer was not hired for several years so I continued providing the bulk of the paramedic training until the position was filled. I continued to conduct classes for Gaston College and even taught an EMT-I class for members of the rescue squads. There was initially a lot of interest, but this faded due to the number of hours required to complete the course. None ever became certified as EMT-Intermediates.

It was about this time that concerns began to rise over the increasing numbers of acquired immunodeficiency syndrome (AIDS) and human immunodeficiency virus (HIV) which could be spread through contact with human bodily fluids. Public service employees such as EMS workers, law enforcement officers, firefighters, and sanitation workers were all at risk for coming in contact with such fluids. After consulting local government officials, I conducted classes in the use of personal protective equipment [PPE] and proper disposal of contaminated items. Initially, there was a question as to why sanitation workers were at risk. After I brought up their potential exposure to blood, needles, and other material in garbage, as well as human waste in water treatment, there was agreement that this group of workers should be included in the target employees. I trained over three thousand county and city employees in how to better protect themselves against exposure.

Today, Gaston County has one of the premier paramedic services in North Carolina with some of the best and most advanced equipment available. GEMS was the first paramedic service in North Carolina to have their in-house recertification program approved by the State of North Carolina. Their training standards are second to none. I am proud to say that I had a small part in their development, and those advances had a large part in saving my life.

My involvement in EMS was not limited to teaching classes. The South Gastonia VFD provided service to a portion of unincorporated southern and southwestern Gaston County. I was a member of this department and had trained many of our members to become EMTs. The closest ambulance base belonged to GEMS and was about four miles from our fire station, but because of the call volume it was rarely available to respond from that location.

Our Fire Chief at the time approached me asking about the possibility of responding to emergency medical calls within our fire district. Because of slow ambulance and rescue unit response to our area, our EMTs could respond to a medical emergency within our district as first responders and provide basic medical aid until an ambulance could arrive to assume further care. Our members could arrive on a call and initiate life-saving measures in less than five minutes instead of a twelve- to fifteen-minute average response time for an ambulance in our part of the county. This response time could be longer or shorter depending upon the origination point of the ambulance.

We approached the Gaston County Commissioners with the idea, and they promptly told us that we needed to first get the approval of the Gaston County Ambulance Association, an organization made up of the eight rescue squads whose members provided ambulance service for the entire county. Here we go again!

Our first meeting with them resulted in an emphatic NO. Again, we were not trying to put any organization out of business and had no interest in providing ambulance transportation service. We wanted to provide patient care to citizens within our fire district until an ambulance, be it GEMS or rescue squad, could arrive on the scene and assume patient care. This service could dramatically reduce response time for a patient to receive vital medical care. We met with the Association numerous times but could not persuade them to allow us to provide first response services. They expressed disapproval when South Gastonia VFD purchased hydraulic rescue equipment known as the "Jaws of Life" and trained in its use. This piece of equipment is used to extricate victims of auto accidents. They asked us to become members of one of the squads thereby allowing us to respond with an ambulance. We thought that might work, but they would not allow us to station the ambulance at our fire station. We would have to respond to their station, some five to six miles away to get an ambulance or crash truck. We felt that this move would potentially lengthen response times and declined. We countered by asking the squad who covered our fire district to use our building as a satellite station. This would allow an ambulance to be closer to our district if it were not already committed to a call. They declined citing that they didn't want an ambulance assigned to a fire station.

With the discussions going nowhere, I felt like further meetings were futile. I was asked by the Chairman of the Rescue Association, "What would you do if rescue squads bought fire trucks, trained as firefighters, and arrived at a house fire in your district before your members arrived?"

I can remember answering, "As long as they were doing the job correctly, I would offer my assistance."

I felt like our ability to improve emergency service in our district was being unfairly ignored. I took a tube of K-Y jelly, a lubricating gel frequently used in the medical profession to make certain types of examinations easier, from my briefcase, placed it on the table, and said, "If you are going to give us the shaft, at least use this to make it a little less painful!"

With that said, our delegation left the meetings. No further meetings were scheduled.

We decided to take our request back to the Commissioners. Members of the Association were there in force. We again presented our case and told the Commissioners of the hesitancy of the Ambulance Association to give us their blessing. We cited lengthy response times as the main reason for our request and reiterated that we had no interest in taking ambulance transportation service away from the squads. I don't remember what comments were made by the Association, but we must have made our point. The Commissioners approved our request to act as medical first responders within our fire response district. We still met with resistance on scenes, but gradually the squads realized that we were not a threat to their existence and that our presence actually helped.

Aside from providing initial care our members on the scene additional staff would help the ambulance personnel with the loading of patients into the ambulances, even carrying their equipment for them while they provided care.

After much controversy, South Gastonia VFD, emerged as the first fire department, paid or volunteer, to provide first responder service in Gaston County. As a result, I prepared a curriculum and began teaching EMT-Basic and EMT-Paramedic classes through our local community college.

After much debate, the county began providing 24-hour emergency service, seven days a week. Volunteers would handle the majority of non-emergency calls and assist on emergencies.

I was retained by the county to provide training for the newly formed paid employees. Over a relatively short period of time the employees of Gaston County Emergency Medical Services [GEMS] went from EMT-Basic to EMT-Paramedic level. Today, GEMS provides emergency ambulance service with simultaneous dispatch of a volunteer unit to all emergency calls. For the most life-threatening emergency calls, a first responder unit from one of the many volunteer or municipal fire departments in the county will also respond thereby reducing response times for medical care.

I always told my EMT and Paramedic students that in order for you to pass my class they "had to be good enough to provide care for me."

Little did I know how true that statement would become. As Eric Hendrix, Gaston County Fire Marshal, told my wife as he drove her to Charlotte to be with me following the accident, "I knew Carl was a big part of developing the current emergency medical system in Gaston County, but he didn't have to check its effectiveness this way."

Chapter 9

Emergency Department Years

My interest in emergency medicine grew and I eventually accepted a position as a PA in the Emergency Department at Gaston Memorial Hospital. I began working there in June 1983. This would prove to be much different than family practice. Instead of treating the mostly non-serious problems of family practice, I was now providing initial assessment and care for such conditions as lacerations, burns, eye injuries, fractures, heart attacks, strokes, stabbings, and gunshot wounds, as well as the run-of-the-mill illnesses. I became quite proficient at suturing, intubating, inserting chest tubes, cutdowns to access deep veins for infusions, inserting external jugular intravenous lines, and working cardiac arrests or 'code blues'.

Once, while working on a rare slow day with Dr. Telzee Foster, we began talking about various things. He mentioned that he had learned a lot about emergency medicine while in Vietnam. I asked him where and when he was there. To my surprise Dr. Foster had also be assigned to the 3rd Surg and had left about six months before I arrived. Small world.

During this time, the training officer for the newly reformed county-supported ambulance service left for other employment. Prior to leaving he was able to train the county EMS employees to the EMT-Intermediate level. This level of certification allowed the EMT to administer IV fluids to a patient prior to arrival at the hospital. I was asked to complete a Basic EMT class for Gaston College when the current instructor left the position open. There, I resumed the training officer's responsibility for GEMS on a part-time basis while continuing to work in the ER at Gaston Memorial. I was able to convince county leaders of the benefits of having paramedics on ambulances, and with the help of some of the ER physicians with whom I worked, conducted the first EMT-Paramedic program in Gaston County. Between my duties as EMS Training Officer and instructing classes for Gaston College, I trained over 3,000 EMS, fire, police, and other interested persons. My wife, Ginger, a registered nurse, also assisted me in teaching these programs.

An integral part of any paramedic service is communication with the hospital. A radio system capable of receiving EKG (electrocardiogram) signals from the paramedic in the field was installed in the ER at GMH.

ER physicians would listen to patient information and give appropriate orders back to the paramedic. After a while the call volume became heavier which further taxed the ER physicians. I partnered with Dr. Gay Houchins, who became GEMS medical director, and we conducted a MICN (Mobile Intensive Care Nurse) course for Registered Nurses in the ER to assume some of the communication duties since a certified

MICN can take verbal or standing orders from the physician and transmit them to the paramedics in the field.

The physician group that employed me at Gaston Memorial lost their contract to provide service forcing me to leave Gaston Memorial Hospital in October 1989 shortly after hurricane Hugo devastated the area. I accepted a position in the emergency department at Mercy Hospital South in Pineville, North Carolina. The patients there generally were not as critical, but we had our moments. I can remember caring for two patients, each of whom were having heart attacks, while the physician was responding to a 'code blue' in the main hospital.

One of the physicians with whom I had worked at Gaston Memorial, Dr. Gary Houchins, also accepted a position at Mercy Hospital. Together, he and I became Advanced Cardiac Life Support (ACLS) instructors and taught several ACLS classes to the nursing staff at Mercy Hospital. I am sorry to say that Dr. Houchins died several years later. I often reflect on the times we worked together.

Shortly after I started working there, Mercy Hospital decided to commission a television commercial to promote the services offered at their two hospitals. They used actors for the physician and patient. Members of the nursing staff served as extras. The actor-patient was to be wheeled in on an ambulance cot with 'CPR in progress'. The actions of the actor-physician and extras were to simulate how the patient would be treated. Since I was working on the day the crew showed up for filming, my job was to act as advisor for the scene dealing with emergency services.

I instructed the actor-physician as to what he needed to say and the actions he needed to perform for the scene to appear believable. After several 'takes' the director didn't feel that the actor-physician was portraying the role adequately. He then asked if I would be interested in giving the position a try. It took a lot of coaxing for me to reluctantly agree to do the part. Two 'takes' later the director was satisfied, and the finished commercial would appear on three local television stations over the next several months. It wasn't a bad commercial, but I still didn't enjoy having my picture taken.

I enjoyed my time at Mercy South. It was later purchased by Carolina's Healthcare Center, which was rebranded as Carolinas Medical Center-Pineville, and is now known as Atrium Health Pineville.

I remained with the hospital for about one year after the purchase. The drive from my house to the hospital was thirty miles one way. The area built up rapidly, and traffic became worse every day requiring more commute time.

In 1994, I was approached by Dr. Robert Barringer, an internal medicine physician in Gastonia whom I had come to know through my work with Dr. Eckbert. Dr. Barringer said that his group, Gaston Internal Medicine, was interested in hiring me to work in their office to provide care to their patients who were acutely ill or had sustained minor injuries rather than sending them to the Emergency Department at

Gaston Memorial where they might otherwise spend several hours waiting for treatment. You can say that was an early form of Urgent Care for patients of the clinic. In October 1994, I accepted that position thus leaving behind that long drive to Pineville.

Chapter 10
Training EMS Responders

My interest in improving the quality of pre-hospital emergency services in Gaston County began in the mid-1970s. Through my work as a volunteer firefighter and as a Physician Assistant I observed firsthand the treatment provided by our paid and volunteer ambulance services. While the care they provided was adequate I felt that pre-hospital care could be greatly improved.

I began by becoming certified as a CPR Instructor for the Red Cross. I taught, or helped teach, numerous classes for paid and volunteer EMS providers, paid and volunteer firefighters, local law enforcement, and members of the public who were interested in learning the technique. As part of my job as a Physician Assistant in the ER, I obtained certifications in Basic Trauma Life Support, Advanced Trauma Life Support, Advanced Cardiac Life Support, Neonatal Emergency Resuscitation Procedure, and other certifications that I used to improve my medical and classroom skills.

This led to my contacting the Continuing Education Section at Gaston Community College. They had developed a program for pre-hospital care providers and were beginning to offer classes for basic Emergency Medical Technician (EMT).

I enrolled in one of the classes and became one of the first State Certified EMTs, and later an EMT Paramedic in Gaston County. I expressed my interest in becoming an instructor for the college and shortly thereafter began conducting basic EMT classes.

In addition to the basic curriculum mandated by the State, I was allowed to add topics that provided students with more knowledge of anatomy, physiology, and medical terminology thus giving them the ability to communicate more professionally with hospital medical staff. The additional training was supported by physicians in the emergency room at Gaston Memorial, but to my surprise was met with resistance to the medical terminology by some members of the local rescue squads.

The local newspaper, *The Gastonia Gazette,* was contacted by someone from a rescue squad complaining that the EMT classes that I had taught had the highest failure rate for the State EMT Examination in the entire state. The newspaper investigated and found that just the opposite was actually true. Gaston College EMT students had one of the highest pass rates in the entire state. After this was printed the resistance subsided, for a while.

The number of both emergency and non-emergency ambulance calls increased over several years. Some members of the all-volunteer rescue squads who had been handling all ambulance calls in Gaston County for several years were beginning to burn out. Response times were getting longer and the number of volunteers available to do the job was dwindling. They were volunteers and should not have been asked to take on that much responsibility.

Part of educating EMTs and first responders included training in the handling of mass casualty events. These events can tax even the best prepared departments and personnel. I would occasionally set up a mock mass casualty event to test and evaluate Gaston County's responders in their preparedness.

In one event I included my daughters, Kelly who was about eight years old and Erin, who was about five years old, as patients. Both were to have been two of about twenty *victims* of a bus accident. The scenario was to have EMS workers triage these patients according to their injuries and transport them to the hospital according to their triage classification. Kelly was lying on the ground and made up with obvious injuries, while Erin was standing near her with injuries that were not so obvious. Responders arrived on the scene and went about the tasks of triage. Things went well except for one problem. Erin was somehow overlooked as a patient but transported in an ambulance with Kelly. The error was not noted until they got to the ER where staff found the hidden injury on Erin.

Chapter 11

Gaston Medical Group Years

I began as the first Physician Assistant for Gaston Internal Medicine on October 1, 1994. It didn't take long for me to be booked up with acute care patients such as lacerations, colds, sore throats, chest pain, and minor orthopedic injuries. Occasionally I would work-in additional patients when they called or showed up at the office requesting treatment. I averaged seeing thirty patients daily. I did not have a designated office, instead I utilized the office of the physician who had been on call the day before thereby having the next day off. I was not required to make hospital rounds so I was able to go home much earlier than I did while working in Cramerton.

In January 1999 the medical practice moved into a new facility and changed its name to Gaston Medical Group. We felt that the new name better described the services we provided. In addition to internal medicine we provided non-invasive cardiology, gastrointestinal consultation, gynecology, and pediatrics. Here, I had my own office, medical assistant, and examination rooms.

Occasionally a patient that was being seen would suffer a cardiac arrest in the office. Utilizing the skills I had learned in the emergency room, I was able to assist in resuscitating the patient. In the time I worked there we had six patients who went into cardiac arrest in the office while I was working. All but one survived to be discharged from the hospital. I enjoyed providing this type of care. It was similar to the care provided in the emergency room without the major trauma. However, I did miss the excitement of major trauma.

We participated in acting as preceptors for PA students from the PA program at East Carolina University in Greenville, North Carolina. Each student would spend six weeks at our clinic learning more about internal medicine. A student had been scheduled to come in May 2006, but since I was not available to help, the secession was cancelled.

Chapter 12

The Accident

The morning of March 29, 2006 was rather foggy. I prepared for work in my usual routine—shower, shave, dress, breakfast, and brush my teeth. My wife did not have to work that morning, so she was at home when I left for work a little earlier than usual since I was going to get a haircut before heading on to work. I kissed her good-bye at about 8 o'clock that morning and climbed into my 1984 GMC Jimmy. I buckled my seatbelt and headed down the driveway. My driveway is graveled and about a quarter of a mile long before it connects to the main road, Crowders Creek Road. I turned right onto Crowders Creek Road and headed the 0.8 miles to U.S. 321 that would take me to my destination in downtown Gastonia. That is the last thing that I would remember for the next eight weeks.

Ginger later told me that she heard a helicopter circling the area that morning after I had left for work. Since we are close to a main highway and along a flight pathway the helicopter from Carolina's Medical Center sometimes takes toward Shelby, she did not dwell on what they were responding to. It was only after someone from my office called her at home inquiring as to my whereabouts that she became concerned. I was never late for work, but it was now after 9am and I had not yet arrived.

At this point, my wife became concerned that there may be a connection between the emergency vehicles that she heard and my absence from work. She tried my cell phone and my pager, but there was no response from either. She also called the barbershop that I usually go to, but they said that I had not been there. Thinking that I may have stopped at an accident to lend assistance, she decided to trace the route that I would have taken. She got into her car and headed down the driveway.

When she reached Crowders Creek Road the fog had lifted enough for her to see that a police car had the road blocked to traffic. She drove up to the patrol car, pulled onto the shoulder of the road and walked up to the officer who told her of an accident just around a curve and out of sight. She asked the officer if he knew what types of vehicles were involved in the accident. He said he did not know. She then began walking toward the scene.

As she approached the accident scene, she saw several fire engines and ambulances. She recognized the rear portion of my Jimmy. Since I was a member of the fire department that would have responded to the accident, she assumed that I had stopped to lend assistance and did not hear my phone or pager. As she got closer, to her horror she saw that the entire front of my Jimmy had been destroyed! Emergency workers were attempting to remove the victim from the other car, who was still entrapped. The other vehicle was a late model Ford Explorer and it too had sustained heavy front-end damage. I was nowhere to be found.

Ginger approached one of the firefighters with my department and asked, "Where's Carl?"

No response from the firefighter. She asked again more sternly, "Where's my husband?!?"

This time the answer was, "They're taking him to Charlotte."

Ginger now knew that the emergency vehicles and helicopter that she heard were responding to the accident in which I had just been involved. As a registered nurse, she also knew that the need for a helicopter, which was typically a time-consuming task requiring a paramedic crew to arrive on the scene, make an evaluation, then call for the helicopter, probably meant that I had sustained serious injuries.

"What's his condition?" she asked.

"I'm not sure," answered the firefighter, "but I think he was talking."

A landing zone for the helicopter had been established about one mile south of the accident in the parking lot of a business on U.S. 321. One of the firefighters who had arrived in his personal vehicle drove my wife to the landing zone, however by the time they arrived the helicopter had lifted off on a course to the Level I Trauma Center at Carolina's Medical Center in Charlotte, a ten-minute flight from the take-off point. Ginger was then taken to the fire station that was just a quarter of a mile north of the landing zone. There she began contacting our daughters. Later she was taken to CMC by Eric Hendrix, an Assistant Fire Marshal for Gaston County. I knew Eric both through the fire department and through Gaston Medical Group where I was employed at the time.

I was unconscious when I arrived at CMC and unaware that I was taken to the Emergency Department, evaluated, and quickly sent to surgery to evaluate intra-abdominal bleeding. The time between an accident and the time trauma services are provided is known as **The Golden Hour**. Every minute past this hour lessens chances for survival of a critically injured patent. I made it to surgery in under an hour.

My daughter Erin was the first of my family to arrive at the hospital since she lived and worked in Charlotte at the time. I later learned that Mike Horne, my department Chief, met her at the hospital. He worked in Charlotte and had been contacted by another member of my department.

Shortly thereafter Ginger arrived at CMC. She got very little information on my condition other than I was extremely critical and had been taken to surgery. By now other family members and friends from my fire department were arriving at CMC to check on my condition. Occasionally someone would emerge from the OR and tell my family that I was still alive, but extremely critical. After some twelve hours in the OR, one of the surgeons caring for me spoke with my family.

He reported that I had suffered massive internal injuries and multiple fractures. My spleen had been ruptured and required removal. He repaired a rupture in my diaphragm. I also sustained tears of my small and large intestines requiring partial resection of both. Both of my lungs were collapsed, and tubes were inserted on both my right side and left to drain any blood and see if the holes responsible for the collapse would seal on their own. Many of my ribs were broken as well as my left hand, pelvis, left hip, bilateral mid-shaft femurs, a fracture of my left ankle, and an open fracture of my right knee. There were also fractures of my left maxilla (cheekbone) and the spinous processes of several of my lumbar vertebrae.

The long bone femoral fractures were stabilized with external fixators. No additional orthopedic surgery would be performed until they were sure that I would survive, and given the extent of my injuries, it was doubtful.

A CT scan of my head revealed a large, left subdural hematoma and multiple small intracranial bleeds. I had also lost several upper left teeth. These are the injuries that they knew at the time.

Ginger would later tell me that when I was rolled out of the OR I had tubes coming out of every orifice and external fixators on both legs. I was intubated and breathing with the aid of a ventilator. IVs were in both arms as well as central IV lines in my both subclavian veins located beneath my clavicles. Through these I was receiving fluid, blood, and blood products such as platelets. I would receive sixty-two units of blood or blood products within the first 24 hours. Some of these products would come from as far away as Miami, Florida.

By the second day I had become so swollen from the fluid and blood transfusions that I was unrecognizable. My brother-in-law, John, could not bear to look at me. My children would constantly ask my wife about my condition. She would explain to them what was taking place. They all knew that I could die at any time. Ginger later told me that my swelling was so bad that she feared that my skin would tear in places. She also told me that during surgery I developed a cardiac irregularity called atrial fibrillation, which causes the upper chambers of the heart to beat erratically and could cause blood clots to develop. If untreated the clot, or clots, could be pumped to my lungs or brain and be fatal. The irregularity was corrected, and I was started on medication in hopes that it would not return.

After several days, a tracheostomy breathing tube was placed into my neck to replace the oral breathing tube that I had initially received.

My family tells me that I would occasionally try to speak to them, but I do not remember those attempts. Although I seemed to be trying to communicate, Ginger knew that I was *not entirely with the program*. I vaguely remember on one occasion attempting to speak but I couldn't because of the tracheostomy tube that was in my airway. Trauma staff placed a device on the tube, called an obturator, that allowed me to say a few words, though I don't know if I could be understood.

The first thing that I can distinctly remember is waking, and with my eyes still closed thinking, *Well, it's time to get up and go to work.*

I opened my eyes, looked around, and thought, *Wait a minute. This is not my bedroom!*

I was in no pain. I tried to get out of bed but could not because my hip fracture had not yet been repaired. Ginger was sitting at my bedside. I listened in disbelief as she told me of the accident. She also told me that it had occurred SEVEN WEEKS earlier. Again, I tried to get out of bed, and again I could not.

"Stop!" she said. "You can't get up. Your left hip is still broken."

"What?" I replied. "How can my hip be broken?" She went on to tell me that the surgery to repair the hip would be major surgery and the doctors wanted to be sure that my nutrition was good before attempting the repair. At this point they were just amazed that I had survived this long.

I was confused. "What happened to me?" I asked. "Where am I, and how long have I been here?" I didn't seem to be in a lot of pain.

"You were in a car accident seven weeks ago. You're in the Trauma Unit at CMC. It appears that someone crossed the center line and hit you head-on," Ginger answered.

I noticed that I had a tube in my left nostril.

"That's how they have been feeding you," Ginger told me. "You've already pulled it out three times. Please leave it alone now," she pleaded.

I had spent thirty years of my life providing care for ill and injured patients, now I was on the receiving end. This was a new experience for me. The seven-week amnesia was a blessing not only for the fact that I don't remember any pain from the injuries, but also that I would have been familiar with the necessary actions used to save my live. Not something that I can imagine, through my role as a first responder, as being fun.

Over the next few days Ginger and my daughters informed me of the injuries that I had sustained:

- a closed head injury
- collapse of both lungs
- cardiac contusion
- a ruptured spleen
- a ruptured diaphragm
- lacerations of my small bowel and large bowel
- fractures of my pelvis, left hip, both femurs, left hand, maxilla, and several spinal vertebrae
- an open fracture of my right knee
- lacerations of my face
- the loss of several upper teeth

I also learned that I had suffered a heart attack as the result of massive blood loss.

I had undergone surgery to remove the spleen and repair the bowel ruptures. These kept bleeding and required two additional surgeries which were performed at my bedside in the Trauma ICU to completely stop the bleeding. The abdominal incision was not closed after the last surgery but was packed with surgical gauze then later closed with a skin graft taken from my left thigh.

I was taken back to surgery several times to repair my orthopedic injuries. Titanium rods were inserted into the shaft of both femurs. The fracture of my right knee was repaired with nine screws. The external fixators were removed. A filter was inserted into my inferior vena cava, the main vein returning blood from the lower part of my body to my heart, to catch any blood clots that might travel from my legs. Bleeding had occurred from my left iliac artery, a main supplier of blood to my pelvis. That bleeding had to be controlled by inserting a coil into that portion of the artery.

The orthopedic surgeries were only performed after the doctors were reasonably sure that I was going to survive my injuries, but these were not the only surgical procedures that I would need to eventually improve my condition.

I had suffered complete failure of my kidneys and liver. My skin became jaundiced and I was placed on hemodialysis and started on insulin. After two weeks on dialysis my organs began to function again. Ginger told me of her elation at the first sign of urine production.

The jaundice subsided as I began producing more urine, and my blood sugar levels, and liver enzymes gradually came down.

After spending seven weeks in the Trauma ICU I was moved to the Post Intensive Care unit. The mere fact that I had survived to this point was a miracle since I had initially been given little chance of surviving. Several physicians told me that on each time they passed my room they expected it to be empty. They could not remember another patient with similar injuries and post-op problems who survived.

On one occasion the staff in the PICU helped me into a Geri chair. This is a recliner-type chair on wheels. Ginger rolled me out of the room and down a hall where she rolled me outside for a few minutes. This was the first I had been out of bed in almost two months. It felt really good!

I have always been a fan of classical music, so while I was still unconscious, my family brought a CD player to my room and played classical CDs as well as music from John Denver and Herb Alpert and the Tijuana Brass. I don't remember hearing the music, but the hospital staff enjoyed coming into my room when the music was playing.

Ginger told me that my room in the Trauma IC Unit had been close to the landing pad for CMC's helicopter. She hoped that the music would drown out the sound of the helicopters fearing that hearing them might make me feel as if I was in Vietnam.

A little while after I gained consciousness, and after the elation of being alive diminished, depression set in. I asked myself:

Why did this happen?

When can I return to work?

Will I ever be able to work?

Will I be able to walk or use my left hand again?

How will I be able to help Ginger?

These were only a few of the questions that plagued me on a daily basis. I could only remember going to bed one night then waking up with these injuries. I had episodes of uncontrollable crying. I had never been hospitalized or had any type of surgery. I never before even suffered a broken bone or had any serious illnesses.

Since I began employment in 1967, I don't think that I missed more than ten days due to illness or injury until the time of the accident. Now, nearly every bone in my body had been broken and I had to face the fact that I almost died as a result of the accident. The healing process was long from being over!

I thought of what my family was going through, especially my wife, Ginger. She is an amazing woman. An only child, Ginger had been the one who took her parents to appointments or to buy groceries since she obtained her driver's license at age sixteen. Neither of her parents had ever acquired their driver's licenses. Prior to Ginger's being able to drive, her family depended on friends or taxis for transportation. However, her father did have a moped that he rode for recreation. Ginger's mother suffered a stroke in 1989 and had been in a nursing home. Her father suffered a stroke after carotid surgery several years later and was in the same nursing home as her mother until his death in 1994. Now this happened to me and she would provide care for me as well. For how long? Who knew? I often thought that she may be better off had I not survived. At least she could get on with a somewhat normal life.

My family told me of the support they received up to this point. For two weeks after the accident members from my department, Gaston EMS, Gastonia Fire Department, or Charlotte Fire Department stayed with my family twenty-four hours every day. Members of my department would go to my house and do yard work. Get Well cards from patients and friends were being sent to me at CMC. My wife taped them to the walls of my room. I was humbled by this show of support.

From these members I began to learn new facts about the accident that nearly took my life. It appears that a late model Ford Expedition traveling toward me crossed the centerline striking my vehicle head-on. There were no skid marks from either vehicle so it's probable that the other vehicle crossed only a few feet in front of me leaving no time to react. The impact spun me around ninety degrees where my vehicle was then struck on the driver's side door by another vehicle. I was entrapped in my vehicle.

A former member of my department, Tim Gunn, came upon the scene moments after it happened. He immediately recognized my vehicle. Using his cell phone, he called a member of my department, Gary Adair, saying "Carl's been in an accident on Crowders Creek Road. It doesn't look good!"

Gary, also a firefighter with the Gastonia Fire Department, was returning home after taking his son to school. He called Travis Bell, a Captain with the Gastonia FD, relaying the information. Travis was just leaving his house which was further down Crowders Creek Road when Gary called him. Travis lives about two miles from the accident and started that way while Gary went to our fire station to start apparatus toward the scene.

By this time Tim had called the 911 system and members were being notified through a pager system. In addition to units from my department the initial activation included dispatch of a basic EMT ambulance, and a paramedic unit to the scene.

Once the first fire apparatus arrived on the scene, they recognized that additional help was needed. Not only was I entrapped in my vehicle but the driver of the other vehicle was also entrapped. Units from neighboring Union Road VFD and Rescue 3 from the Gastonia FD were dispatched.

Word of my accident began to spread. An ambulance and crash truck from our station in Bessemer City responded, as did Eric Hendrix from the Gaston County Fire Marshal's office.

My injuries appeared more serious than those of the other driver so efforts to extricate me began while other members attended to the other driver until additional help arrived. The 'Jaws of Life,' which we have on our apparatus, was used to remove my driver's side door that had been crumpled from its normal width down to about twenty inches. After the driver's door was removed the rescuers discovered that my feet were pinned beneath the dashboard making my removal from the driver's side impossible. In order to free my feet and legs they immediately moved to the passenger's side, removed the door, passenger's seat, and center console.

By this time Rescue 3, other units from Union Road, and ambulances from Dallas Rescue, Gaston EMS, and my own department had arrived. Rescuers worked to extricate the driver of the other vehicle. Paramedics accessed the other vehicle driver and me to start IV lines and stabilize fractures. Tina Caudel, one of the paramedics on the scene determined that my injuries warranted treatment at a Trauma Center and called for the helicopter from CMC. Travis later told me that I was trying to talk to him, but he could not understand what I was trying to say.

Once out of my vehicle I was loaded into the ambulance from Gaston EMS, which is the county's paramedic service, and taken to the designated landing zone on U.S. 321 South.

As the helicopter landed the paramedics later told me that I recognized that I was having difficulty breathing and asked to be intubated. The driver of the other vehicle was taken to Gaston Memorial Hospital and from there transferred to CMC. I learned later on that she was in a room several doors down from where I was in the Trauma ICU.

I also learned that of all the personnel who responded to my accident from Crowders Mountain VFR, Union Road VFD, Gastonia FD, Gaston EMS, and Dallas Rescue I had provided some type of training to all - but one. Her name was Tina Caudel and is the paramedic with Gaston EMS who actually called for the helicopter. I feel that this act was the single pre-hospital care call that was responsible for saving my life.

Eric Hendrix told my wife that he knew that I had been an integral part of setting up the current EMS system in Gaston County, but that I didn't have to test its effectiveness in this way.

Chapter 13

Rehabilitation and Recovery

By June 6, 2006 I had improved enough to be moved to a rehabilitation facility and was transferred to Courtland Terrace in Gastonia. It so happened that my mother-in-law was in the assisted living wing of Courtland. This would make visitation for Ginger so much easier.

I also had visits from the physicians and staff of Gaston Medical Group, members of my fire department, patients that I have treated, local EMS, fire management and medical personnel, the Gaston County Sheriff Alan Cloninger, church members, and some of the staff from Gaston College.

Ginger moved the cards that I had received in Charlotte to my room at Courtland. By now there were enough to nearly cover every wall of my room. The staff at Courtland told me that they had never seen as many cards, and more would be coming.

I was still unable to get out of bed without assistance. My right knee was placed in a continuous passive motion device for twenty to thirty minutes several times daily in hopes of improving the range of motion of the injured area. I had sustained fractures of my left 3rd and 4th metacarpals (the bones in the hand), and now I was unable to flex my fingers in order to grasp objects due to scar tissue that had formed in the joints. My left hand was mostly numb indicating an injury to my brachial plexus, a group of several nerves supplying my arm and hand. Physical therapy was being provided in an attempt to improve my grip.

My left hip was still broken so I was not allowed to bear weight on my left leg. My left foot was numb, and I was unable to bend it up toward my head, a condition known as foot drop. This indicates an injury to the sciatic and peroneal nerves. Since I was a medical professional the physicians and nursing staff could speak to me in medical terms. I am still not sure if that was good or bad.

During this time, I still had no recall of anything for the seven weeks after the accident. I am convinced that this is a good thing since I also didn't recall any pain. Amnesia is a wonderful analgesic!

We gradually increased the amount of physical therapy on my legs and left hand. After several follow-up visits with the orthopedists in Charlotte, they allowed me to begin some minimal weight bearing on my left leg which still had an un-united fracture in the hip. This allowed me to be helped from the bed so I could try to use a walker. I had lost so much muscle tone that at first the mere act of sitting was difficult. For several weeks, a lifting device was used to move me from bed to a chair and later a wheelchair.

Since Courtland Terrace is closer to home some additional members of my fire department and other friends began to visit. They may have visited me at CMC, but I don't remember the visit if they did.

During the time I was in Courtland my mother was admitted to Gaston Memorial Hospital for treatment of several chronic problems that had plagued her for many years. During her hospitalization she developed pneumonia and became seriously ill. By this time, I was able to sit in a wheelchair. I was able to use a power chair from Courtland and, accompanied by Ginger and a staff nurse from Courtland, I rode across the parking lot separating the two facilities to visit my mother. Her condition continued to deteriorate, and she passed away in August 2006.

Melanie and Wayne Massagee, who are members of my fire department, transported Ginger and me to my mom's funeral in one of our ambulances. Afterwards they took me to my father's house where we visited for a while. This was the first time that I had been to his house since my accident. It was a bittersweet accomplishment. From Dad's living room window, I could see my own house, but we did not go there.

I had to go to Charlotte at least once every week for follow-up appointments. Members from my department would take their own time to transport me to and from those appointments by ambulance. Even though I asked them to bill me for the service they refused to do so.

In September 2006, my fire department's personnel transported me in one our ambulances to the grand opening of our new fire station that had been under construction. I had served as chairman of the building committee responsible for the design of the new building. I had been taking pictures of building progress and posted them on our website. My accident prevented me from personally seeing the building completed.

On October 11, 2006, seven months after the accident, I was discharged home. Ginger had worked hard to make our home accessible for me. She moved a hospital bed in that had been used by my mother. She also had a ramp built from our driveway to our front porch in anticipation of future use of a wheelchair. Members from my department transported me home from Courtland Terrace. That day was the first time I had been in my home since the accident in March 2006. I still was unable to walk, but I could slide transfer myself to a wheelchair.

Support for Ginger and me continued long after my discharge from Courtland. The staff in the ER at Gaston Memorial organized a Bar-b-Que benefit at Bradley Memorial United Methodist Church, a small local church to help cover some of the medical costs. Their hard work raised enough money to purchase the power chair that I use today.

My daughters and GMH ER organized blood drives in my honor and later Erin organized a yard sale that raised money to help cover medical bills not covered by insurance.

Ginger worked with a nurse in the ER who is a member of Hull's Grove Baptist Church in Vale, North Carolina, a small town in Lincoln County. Neither Ginger nor I are members of this church, yet they sent cards to me every week for several years without fail following my accident. I have learned of many more churches that have included me on their prayer lists including one in Georgia.

A friend of mine, Vernon 'Bernie' Bernhardt, with whom I had attended PA school, called me at home. He had watched the news of the accident unfold on local TV. His daughter works at CMC and kept Bernie updated on my condition. Bernie lives and has worked in the Salisbury area of North Carolina since graduating from PA school. He is one of the friends with whom I made fishing trips while in Charleston. We have stayed in contact with each other since my accident and occasionally get together for a meal.

I gradually became able to transfer myself to my wheelchair and could guide myself around my house. I could even ride outside and visit my father who lived nearby. It would be several more months before I would be able to walk into his house. I visited frequently until he died in February 2010 at the age of 86.

In late February 2007 I was scheduled to have a left hip replacement and reconstruction of my pelvis. Because of the nature of my hip fracture the replacement would not allow my left leg to function in a normal way. Rather the femoral head would need to be attached to the posterior portion of what used to be the hip socket. This would leave me with a slight external rotation of my left foot. I told Ginger that the leg I set for the goat rotated out for him, and now does mine. Karma!

The fact that I cannot recall any of the events of the accident or the following seven weeks now seems a blessing. Back at the hospital, as I was waking up from the anesthesia, I remember telling Ginger that I couldn't imagine being able to tolerate the amount of pain that I suffered at the time of the accident when compared to the pain I now had. That was only a few days before being discharged home.

Ginger took great care of me. She changed my dressings as we had been instructed. I had little sensation in the area of my left hip in part due to the surgery. However, after about a week Ginger began to notice some discoloration to the fluid from the drainage tube in my hip that until now had been clear yellow or slightly bloody. Additional discolored fluid began seeping from the incision site after another day or two. Despite the lack of pain that is usually associated with tissue infections, we were concerned that the hip had become infected and with it the possibility of needing to remove all of the hardware that had just been used to repair my hip and pelvis. We called for ambulance transportation to CMC. Wayne and Melanie Massagee showed up with one of our department's ambulances to make the trip.

Once in the ER at CMC I was evaluated. The ER physician inserted a long, sterile cotton-tipped applicator into the wound releasing a copious amount of pus and bloody fluid confirming our suspicions of the presence of tissue infection.

So, on March 10, 2007, less than one year after the accident, I found myself being prepared for surgery again. This time in an attempt not only to treat the infection, but also to save the hardware previously used to repair my hip and pelvis. It would take an additional procedure two days later before Dr. Jon Masonis, the orthopedic surgeon, would feel that enough infected and necrotic tissue had been removed to treat the infection successfully.

At least for now, the hardware would remain in place and I would be discharged home after placement of a percutaneous intravascular catheter (PIC line) in my upper left arm. The PIC line would allow Ginger to administer IV antibiotics to me twice daily to eradicate the existing bacteria and to prevent its return. If the infection returned the hardware used to rebuild my pelvis and replace my left hip would need to be removed so that the infection could be treated more aggressively. If the hardware required removal, there would be little chance of another attempt to repair the fractures.

With some apprehension, we waited to see the outcome. But, fortunately I continued to improve and there was no evidence that infection was returning.

I was now able to transfer to a wheelchair more easily and began using a wheelchair transport service to take me to my frequent follow-up appointments in Charlotte. Quickly this proved to be an expensive service that was not covered by insurance. I was unable to get into a standard car, truck, or van because I could not yet bend my knees far enough.

Not knowing how much longer I would need the wheelchair transport service which was running $300 to $500 monthly Ginger began looking into lift vans. She was persistent, but I remained resistant to the purchase of such an expensive vehicle, confident that I would not need the transport service much longer. Reluctantly, however, I began to realize that my injuries were going to require specialized transport for a long time and agreed to the purchase. We could not have made a better move.

Erin helped Ginger locate the ideal vehicle for my needs. It has a lowered floor and a ramp on the passenger's side that lowers with the touch of a button. I could drive my power chair up the ramp and was then secured with straps attached to the chair while my seatbelt kept me in the chair. After almost a year I became able get myself into the front seat of the van by maneuvering either my power chair or a walker to the passenger's side door and sitting on the seat. Ginger would then load my walker or drive my power chair into the van. Now I could go places with Ginger and even travel to Durham to visit Kelly and Eric. I could even drive the van for short distances.

Between February 2007 and January 2008, I underwent eight separate surgical procedures, including three procedures on my left hip. These did not include the procedures associated with the initial attempts to save my life.

In July 2007 I underwent surgery to remove scar tissue from the joints of my left hand and fingers. The following month I had the Achilles tendon in my left leg lengthened to correct contractures of that tendon that caused a condition known as 'foot-drop'.

I now wear a brace on my left leg to correct the foot drop and a two-inch build up on my right shoe to make up for the length of my right leg lost in the repair of my knee fracture. To this day if asked how tall I am I reply, "Without shoes I am five-foot-eleven when standing on my left foot and five-foot-nine when standing on my right."

Twice in December 2007 attempts were made to remove an eight millimeter stone in my right ureter that was related to the months of inactivity following the accident. On the second attempt the stone was located and broken up with a laser.

On December 5, 2007 I was fitted for dental braces to correct mal-alignment of my teeth resulting from the accident. I wore these braces for two years then I was fitted with a partial denture to replace the teeth I lost on the day of the accident..

In January 2008, I underwent a tendon transfer and release of a carpal tunnel entrapment in my left hand. I hoped that after physical therapy, I would regain some of the ability to grasp with my left hand.

At this time, as I was able to get out more, it seemed that Ginger and I could not go anywhere that one or both of us was not recognized by someone who we had either trained or treated in the past. Former patients told me that they credit me with saving their lives because I had found and treated serious problems in their early stages. This is humbling for me, but I don't feel that I did anything different than any other healthcare provider would have done. I would never have dreamed that our work in the past would have touched so many lives.

I am frequently asked if I had any out-of-body experiences, or if I saw any bright lights during my unconsciousness. To this I can only answer, *no*. This doesn't mean that I do not believe that other people have experienced such episodes, just that I didn't.

I have not attended church services during the past several years as I should have, but I do believe in God and the healing power of prayer. To the latter I am a living testament. However, I do not believe that it was my God's will that I be involved in the accident that nearly took my life. Just like I do not believe that it's God's will that one child die a violent death or another die from starvation. Bad things happen!

I don't think that all bad things can be prevented, but there are things that we can do to help prevent some of them. Be kind to one another. Support law enforcement and military personnel. Wear seatbelts. Drive defensively. Do not drive after drinking alcohol, taking narcotics, or if sleepy. Support charitable and volunteer organizations. Become a volunteer with a local agency.

Some individuals may say that they can't fight fire or take care of the infirmed and injured. How do you know until you try? Believe me there is no better feeling than the one that comes from providing a service to your community, even if you receive no thanks for your efforts.

Some people will say that they don't have time to volunteer. Most everyone that I know who is currently giving their time to a volunteer agency works forty or more hours weekly. What would happen if these people suddenly didn't have time? If nothing else happened local property taxes would go through the roof as local government struggled to hire personnel to do the jobs previously performed by volunteers.

As I sit reflecting on my recovery, many anniversaries of the accident have come and gone. I hope that I will soon awaken from this nightmare and get on with my life. In June 2008, while Ginger and I were shopping at a local home improvement store, a friend of mine, Jimmy Horne, who I have not seen in several years, recognized me and we began talking. Jimmy has worked for years as a photographer for a local television station. He told me that he was shooting film of the accident when the helicopter landed. He also told me that as I was loaded into the helicopter that he never expected to see me alive again.

In late 2009 I began running low-grade fever. I had no severe pain although I did experience some superficial discomfort over my left iliac crest. After consulting my infectious disease physician, a CT of my left hip was ordered. It showed a collection of fluid in that area. This was drained and cultured. I was placed on an additional antibiotic to combat the infection. Several weeks later, however, there had been significant swelling over my left iliac crest area. I was still running fever and by now was feeling very weak with the slightest exertion. In January 2010 I underwent surgical exploration of the area, and a drain was inserted to prevent further fluid accumulation in the area. Another PIC line was inserted and remained in place for eight weeks. Through this line Ginger would administer antibiotics daily. With the infection apparently abated the PIC line was removed.

I continue to improve with my walking ability although my blood pressure drops after standing for only ten or fifteen minutes. My primary care physician has tried numerous medications and compression stockings to overcome the problem, but with no improvement. The amount of damage to my peripheral leg veins prevents them from constricting normally to help maintain a normal blood pressure. This has proven to be my main obstacle to returning to work as a Physician Assistant.

Chapter 14

Beyond the Golden Hour

After any bad event one looks for anything good to emerge. From an EMS standpoint my accident, the decisions made in the pre-hospital setting for handling the incident, were responsible for changes in how the emergency helicopter transport is handled in Gaston County.

Prior to March 29, 2006 a member of an ambulance crew in Gaston County had to be on scene, make an evaluation of the patient, contact the EMS Shift Supervisor, and relay patient information. The EMS Supervisor would make the final decision on requesting helicopter transport to the Level I trauma center at Carolina's Medical Center. This could be a fatal, time consuming decision, especially when considering the Golden Hour.

A critically injured patient's best chance for survival lies with that patient receiving definitive treatment in a Level I Trauma Center *within one hour of the time of the accident.*

The clock starts at the time of the accident, not with the arrival of EMS units. At the time of my accident the average response time for an ambulance in Gaston County was from six to eight minutes. Tack onto that, time to evaluate of the patient, twenty minutes or more for extrication if needed, time to contact the EMS Supervisor to authorize the helicopter, then the travel time for the helicopter to the scene, and from the scene onward to the hospital. The total travel time can exceed thirty minutes. Now, it becomes easy to see how that first hour can go by dangerously fast.

Within two weeks of my accident changes were made that now calls for the automatic dispatch of helicopter transport for all auto accidents, gunshot wounds, and other serious forms of trauma in Gaston County. The helicopter will be dispatched to a pre-designated landing zone near the incident. Once an EMS unit arrives on the scene and evaluates the patient, the helicopter will be cancelled if not needed.

A popular site for rock climbers, Crowders Mountain, lies within Gaston County. Four or five times a year a climber will fall from one of the mountain's cliffs and may fall as far as 150 feet, although 30-50 feet is average. These falls usually result in difficulty for rescuers to reach the area where the patient can be easily accessed. Typically, a team from fire, rescue, and EMS must climb up to, or rappel down to, the patient. Accessing the patient typically takes over an hour. Once accessed, the patient is evaluated and packaged (prepared for removal from the scene), then carried to a waiting ambulance for transport.

More often than not in this type rescue, the Golden Hour has long passed before definitive care can be started. But with automatic dispatch of the helicopter now being the standard, the helicopter can be standing by at the designated landing zone long before the patient arrives for transport.

From a personal standpoint, in my life after my accident, I feel that I am much closer with my family. I think that all families become comfortable with each other, and perhaps take each other for granted, at least somewhat, but I can't imagine being without my wife, Ginger, or either of our daughters.

Ginger is a wonderful and amazing woman. Not only is she the mother of my two children, she worked full time as a nurse in the ER at Gaston Memorial for over forty years. She also founded the local chapter of Mothers Against Drunk Driving, and has put up with me for over forty years. Sure, we still have disagreements, but we do more things together than we did prior to the accident. I survived to see my grandchildren. I have tried to become the best husband, father, and person that I can be.

I feel that my faith in God is stronger. I have seen, firsthand, the power of prayer; not only from my family, but also from friends and people I didn't know.

As time moves along, few things remain the same. The building that housed the Cramerton Clinic is now a coffee shop. Gaston Memorial Hospital is now CaroMont Regional Medical Center. Carolina's Medical Center has become Atrium Health. Mercy South is now Atrium Health Pineville. Gaston Medical Group is now CaroMont Internal Medicine. The building that housed South Gastonia VFD is now a new and used tire business. The building for the Chapel Grove VFD is now a church. The property being used by Bessemer City Rescue was returned to the city.

The auto-dispatch of a helicopter to accidents was discontinued several years ago when CaroMont became a Level III Trauma Center. Of the eight rescue squads that existed at the time of my accident, only two remain as independent organizations. The others either merged with a fire department or went out of business completely. This was due primarily to the increasing lack of people willing to volunteer their time for the benefit of the community. The Myers mill was torn down and a metal storage shed sales business now occupies that space.

Today, people are all about the dollar and not volunteer-oriented. Most now want to be paid for their services. Of the seventeen volunteer fire departments in Gaston County, almost all now employ either part-time or full-time firefighters who are also certified as EMTs to provide response for first aid and medical calls. This includes Crowders Mountain Fire and Rescue. The duplex that I shared at 1711 Savannah Highway in Charleston has been torn down and an auto parts store now occupies that space.

In the time since my accident, I have become interested in genealogy. During my research I have been able to trace my ancestry back twelve generations to the mid-1500s in Germany and England. Some of my ancestors were activists in the Revolutionary War. Valentine Leonard, my sixth great-grandfather, and Patrick Henry, my fifth great uncle, played important roles in our independence. Thomas Sumpter, my third great grandfather, who was a brigadier general in the Revolutionary War, had Fort Sumpter in Charleston, South Carolina named for him. There were also numerous ancestors who fought and died in every war that the United States has been involved in.

Many years have passed since my life-changing accident. I ponder what might have been had I not been so severely injured.

Would I still be working?

Would I still be involved with the fire department?

Would I still be teaching EMS classes?

From where I live, I can hear fire trucks and ambulances responding to calls for help. Although I still miss responding, those feeling are not as strong as they were in 2006.

When Ginger and I drive past the location where the accident occurred, which is every time we drive up Crowders Creek Road, she says, "I hate this road!"

She relives unpleasant memories with each trip past the area. Passing the accident scene does not bother me. I can only assume that it is because I have no memory of the accident.

I have asked Ginger and my daughters many times to write down their perspectives on the accident and subsequent events, but they have been resistant to do so because reliving those events is just too painful for them.

To this day, I am humbled by comments former patients and acquaintances make to me about the effect I had on their lives. I thank them but tell them that I was only doing my job.

I recently learned that as a result of my being a Physician Assistant and teaching EMT and Paramedic classes, three of my former students have gone on to become Physician Assistants and at least two have become Registered Nurses.

I look back at these events and how they, along with help from Tim Gunn, Travis Bell, Union Road VFD, Crowders Mountain VFR, Dallas Rescue, and GEMS, especially Tina Caudel, among others, came together at just the right time to help me survive **Beyond the Golden Hour.**

Acknowledgements

Special thanks to Tina Caudle who stuck to her guns when she requested helicopter evacuation, because of my injuries, to a Level I trauma center. I credit her quick action with saving my life. I also want to acknowledge all of those who participated in my rescue.

Thanks to Marsha Burris and Donna Chinnis who lent their expertise in editing and publishing to make this book a reality.

Resources

Gaston County Emergency Medical Services GEMS

       (GastonEMS.com)

Crowders Mountain Volunteer Fire and Rescue

       (CMVFR.com)

Union Road VFD

       (unionroadvfd.com)

Dallas Rescue

       (dallasrescue.com)

Gastonia Fire Department

       (gastoniafiredepartment.com)

3rd Surgical Hospital

       (3rdSurgicalHospital.com)

Groves, Joel. "Could Quick Action Have Saved Four?"

       The Gaston Gazette. Aug 2, 1979

Barber, Karen. "Gaston Tops State EMT Test Average."

       The Gaston Gazette. Sept 21, 1982

Stowe, Carl. "Upgrade the Service and Let Fees Help".

       The Gaston Gazette. Sept 11, 1983

The Author

Carl Stowe is a retired Volunteer Firefighter, Physician Assistant, and Emergency Medical Professional. He has been married to Ginger Ann Bollinger Stowe for forty-three years. They have two daughters, two sons-in-law, two grandsons and two granddaughters. Carl and Ginger live on Stowe Family land in Gaston County that has passed down through four generations. Through Carl's interest in genealogy, he has traced his family lineage to the Revolutionary War, the Sumpters of South Carolina, and Patrick Henry who is his fifth great uncle.

CPSIA information can be obtained
at www.ICGtesting.com
Printed in the USA
BVHW090542170421
605144BV00015B/752/J

9 780991 444397